really easy chorals

About this book

really easy chorals are the easiest introduction to choral singing. Five great songs are arranged for unison singing in a comfortable range, with an optional harmony part.

The second part can be sung or omitted, depending on the choir's forces and/or preference. It could be used to stretch more confident members of the group. This is notated by a smaller notehead on the same stem as the vocal line – the second voice sings with the main vocal line where a split is not indicated.

Vocal ranges are given at the start of each song, and where the second voice does not go as high, this is placed in parentheses.

Wise Publications
part of The Music Sales Group
London / New York / Paris / Sydney / Copenhagen / Berlin / Madrid / Hong Kong / Tokyo

Contents

Published by
Wise Publications
14-15 Berners Street,
London W1T 3LJ, UK.

Exclusive Distributors:
Music Sales Limited
Distribution Centre, Newmarket Road,
Bury St Edmunds, Suffolk IP33 3YB, UK.
Music Sales Pty Limited
20 Resolution Drive, Caringbah,
NSW 2229, Australia.

Order No. AM999889
ISBN 978-1-84938-462-9

Arranged by Jonathan Wikeley.
Edited by Rachel Lindley.
Cover design by Ruth Keating.

Backing tracks by Guy Dagul
Vocals by Rachel Lindley
CD mixed and mastered by Jonas Persson

Printed in the EU.

Your Guarantee of Quality
As publishers, we strive to produce every book to the
highest commercial standards.
This book has been carefully designed to minimise awkward
page turns and to make playing from it a real pleasure.
Particular care has been given to specifying acid-free, neutral-sized paper
made from pulps which have not been elemental chlorine bleached.
This pulp is from farmed sustainable forests and was
produced with special regard for the environment.
Throughout, the printing and binding have been planned to
ensure a sturdy, attractive publication which should give years of enjoyment.
If your copy fails to meet our high standards,
please inform us and we will gladly replace it.

www.musicsales.com

really easy chorals

Vocal range

The Climb

Words & Music by Jessica Alexander & Jon Mabe

* Cue notes in bars 1–10 show rhythmic alteration for second verse. Optional second part begins at bar 11.

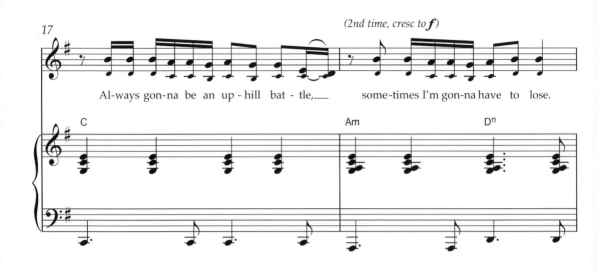

Al-ways gon-na be an up - hill bat - tle,___ some-times I'm gon-na have to lose.

Ain't a-bout how fast I get there, ain't a-bout what's wait-ing on the oth - er

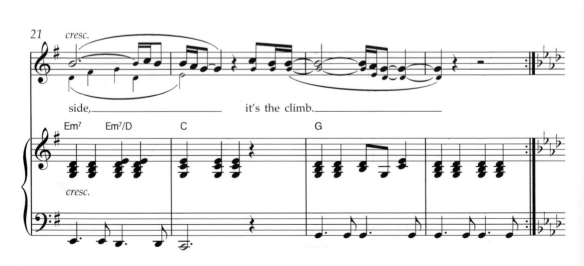

side,_____ it's the climb._____

There's al-ways gon-na be an-oth-er moun - tain,__ I'm al-ways gon-na wan-na make it move.

Al-ways gon-na be an up-hill bat - tle,__ some - times I'm gon-na have to lose.

Ain't a-bout how fast I get there__ ain't a-bout what's wait-ing on the oth - er

side,_____ it's the climb._____

9

Vocal range

track 2 (demo)
track 7 (backing)

The Salley Gardens

Words by William Butler Yeats
Traditional Music

bid me— take love ea - sy, as the leaves grow on— the— tree: But—
bid me— take life ea - sy, as the grass grows on— the— weirs: But—

I be-ing young and— fool - ish, with— her would— not a-
I was— young and— fool - ish, and— now am—— full of

-gree.
tears.   In a

Vocal range

track 3
(demo)
track 8
(backing)

Rule the World

Words & Music by Mark Owen, Gary Barlow,
Jason Orange & Howard Donald

* Cue notes in bars 13–21 can be added as suits the group/performance. A suggestion is that it is omitted for the first two choruses, and added after the *segno*.

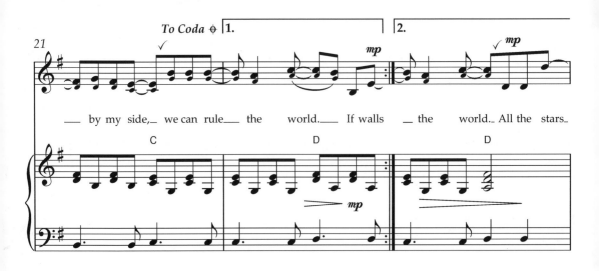

by my side,__ we can rule__ the world.__ If walls __ the world.. All the stars__

__ are com-ing out__ to-night, their light-ing up the sky__ to-night__ for__ you,__

for__ you. All the stars__ are com-ing out__ to-night, their light - ing up the sky to-night__

for__ you,__   for you,_____   oh._____

__ the   world. All the stars_____ are com-ing   out_ to night,__they're

light-ing up the sky__ to-night,   for__ you,_   for__ you.._(All the stars)

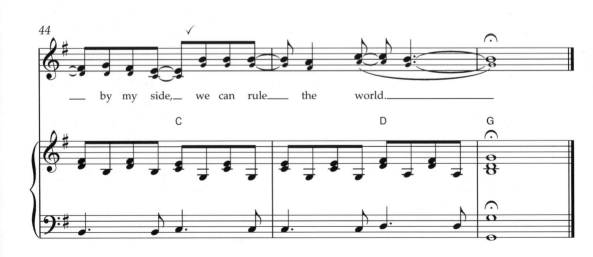

Vocal range

Wade in the water

Traditional

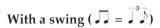

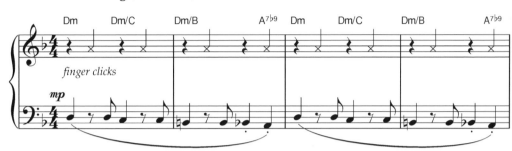

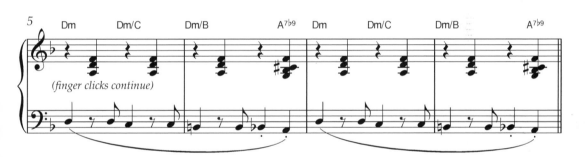

For clarity, the second part is shown in this song on an additional stave. Add 2nd part after repeat.

19

Vocal range

track 5 (demo)
track 10 (backing)

Thank You for the Music

Words & Music by Benny Andersson & Björn Ulvaeus

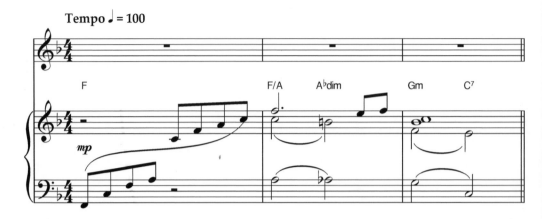

I'm noth-ing spe - cial, in fact I'm a bit__ of a bore.__
Mo-ther says I__ was a dan - cer be - fore__ I could walk.__

If I tell a joke,_ you've pro - ba - bly heard it be - fore.
She says I be- gan__ to sing long be - fore__ I could talk.

loud.
fan.

loud,
fan, } So I say, thank you for the mu - sic, the songs I'm sing-ing,

C   F   Gm   C⁹   F

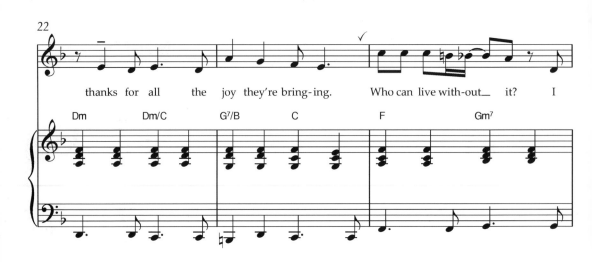

thanks for all the joy they're bring-ing. Who can live with-out__ it? I

Dm   Dm/C   G⁷/B   C   F   Gm⁷

ask in all hon-es - ty,___ What would life be?___ With-out a song__

A⁷   Dm   B♭   B♭m

Track Listing

1 **The Climb** DEMONSTRATION

2 **The Salley Gardens** DEMONSTRATION

3 **Rule The World** DEMONSTRATION

4 **Wade In The Water** DEMONSTRATION

5 **Thank You For The Music** DEMONSTRATION

6 **The Climb** BACKING TRACK

7 **The Salley Gardens** BACKING TRACK

8 **Rule The World** BACKING TRACK

9 **Wade In The Water** BACKING TRACK

10 **Thank You For The Music** BACKING TRACK

The Climb
(Alexander/Mabe)
Stage Three Music Limited/Warner/Chappell Artemis Music Limited

The Salley Gardens
(Traditional)
Dorsey Brothers Music Limited

Rule The World
(Owen/Barlow/Orange/Donald)
EMI Music Publishing Limited/Sony/ATV Music Publishing (UK) Limited/
Universal Music Publishing Limited

Wade In The Water
(Traditional)
Dorsey Brothers Music Limited

Thank You For The Music
(Andersson/Ulvaeus)
Bocu Music Limited